Whitsun Glory

Twelve pieces for organ to celebrate the Ascension & Pentecost

Kevin Mayhew

We hope you enjoy the music in *Whitsun Glory*.
Further copies of this and other collections of outstanding organ music
are available from your local music shop or Christian bookshop.

In case of difficulty, please contact the publisher direct by writing to:

The Sales Department
KEVIN MAYHEW LTD
Rattlesden
Bury St Edmunds
Suffolk IP30 0SZ

Phone 01449 737978
Fax 01449 737834

Please ask for our complete catalogue of outstanding Church Music.

Front Cover: *Pentecost* (fragment). Studio of Luis Borrassa.
Reproduced by kind permission of Christies' Images, London.

Cover designed by Graham Johnstone and Veronica Ward.

First published in Great Britain in 1996 by Kevin Mayhew Ltd

ISBN 0 86209 772 X
Catalogue No: 1400078

Music Editors: Rosalind Dean and Donald Thomson
Music setting by Harriet Lawrence

Printed and bound in Great Britain by
Caligraving Limited Thetford Norfolk

Contents

		Page
A Recessional for Pentecost	Colin Mawby	43
Fanfare for Pentecost	Christopher Tambling	5
Improvisation on Veni, Creator Spiritus	Noel Rawsthorne	8
Non vos relinquam orphanos	Andrew Gant	34
O Comforter, draw near	Colin Hand	22
O Holy Spirit, Lord of Grace	June Nixon	12
Peace I leave with you	Stanley Vann	24
Postlude on Llanfair	Dom Andrew Moore	38
Prelude on Salisbury	Philip Moore	32
Spiritus Domini	Richard Lloyd	28
The Dove Descending	Malcolm Archer	16
Veni, Creator Spiritus	Richard Proulx	19

About the Composers

Malcolm Archer (*b.*1952), formerly Organist and Master of the Choristers at Bristol Cathedral, is a recitalist, composer and conductor. He is now Head of Chapel Music at Clifton College, Bristol.

Andrew Gant (*b.*1963) is Director of Music in Chapel at Selwyn College, Cambridge. He also directs the *Light Blues* vocal ensemble and is Musical Director of the Thursford Christmas concerts. He has worked extensively as an arranger for both radio and television.

Colin Hand (*b.*1929) is a composer of choral, orchestral and chamber music for both professional and amateur players.

Richard Lloyd (*b.*1933) was Assistant Organist of Salisbury Cathedral and successively Organist of Hereford and Durham Cathedrals. He now divides his time between examining and composing.

Colin Mawby (*b.*1936) composes in many forms. He was previously Choral Director at Radio Telefís Éireann, the national broadcasting authority in the Republic of Ireland, and Master of the Music at Westminster Cathedral.

Dom Andrew Moore (*b.*1954) is a Benedictine Monk at Downside Abbey, near Bath. He studied at the Royal Academy of Music and at Cambridge University.

Philip Moore (*b.*1943) is Organist and Master of the Music at York Minster.

June Nixon is Organist and Director of the Choir at St Paul's Cathedral, Melbourne, Australia. She also teaches at the Melbourne University School of Music.

Richard Proulx (*b.*1937) is a composer, conductor and organist. He was Music Director at the Cathedral of the Holy Name in Chicago for fourteen years. His ensemble *The Cathedral Singers* is well-known for its series of recordings of both early music and original works.

Noel Rawsthorne (*b.*1929) was Organist of Liverpool Cathedral for twenty-five years and City Organist and Artistic Director at St George's Hall, Liverpool. He was also Senior Lecturer in Music at St Katharine's College, Liverpool until his retirement in 1993. In 1994 he was awarded an honorary degree of Doctor of Music by the University of Liverpool.

Christopher Tambling (*b.*1964) is the Director of Music at Glenalmond College in Perthshire.

Stanley Vann (*b.*1910) was successively Organist at Chelmsford and Peterborough Cathedrals.

FANFARE FOR PENTECOST

Christopher Tambling

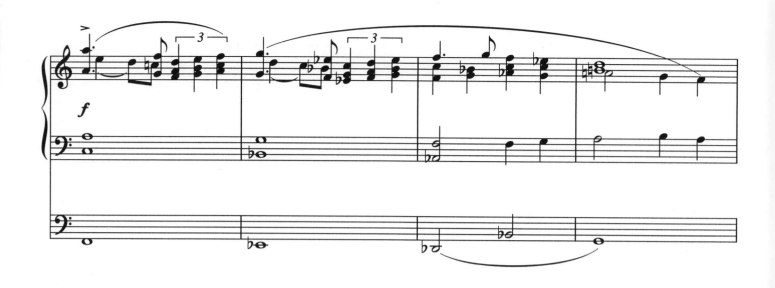

Fine

FANFARE FOR PENTECOST

Christopher Tambling

D.C. al Fine

IMPROVISATION ON VENI, CREATOR SPIRITUS

Noel Rawsthorne

O HOLY SPIRIT, LORD OF GRACE

June Nixon

14

THE DOVE DESCENDING

Malcolm Archer

Slow (♪ = 69)

Ch. 8' 1' (or tierce)

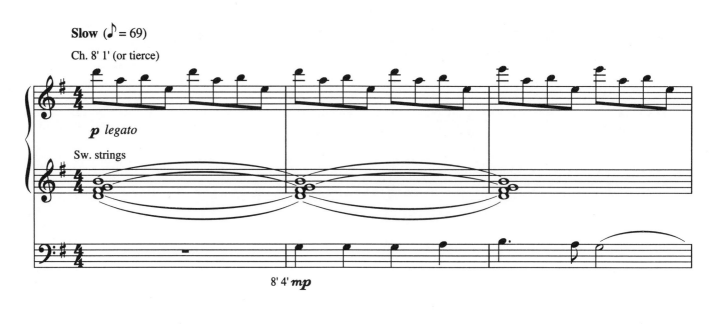

p *legato*

Sw. strings

8' 4' **mp**

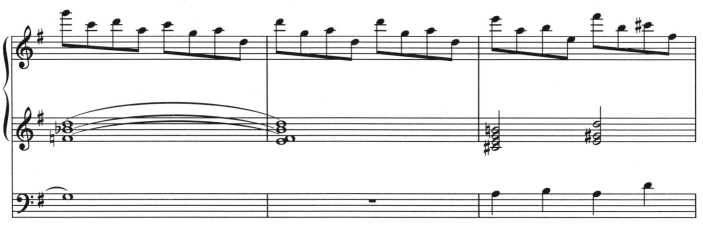

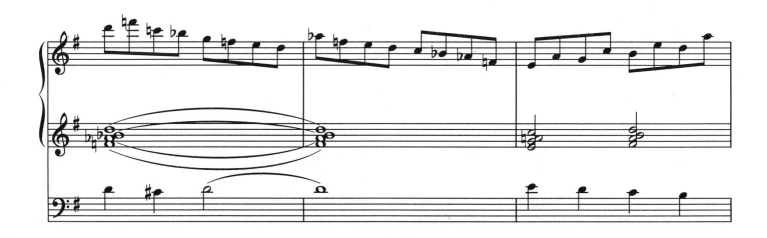

rall. poco a poco

dim.

ppp

32'

18

VENI, CREATOR SPIRITUS

Richard Proulx

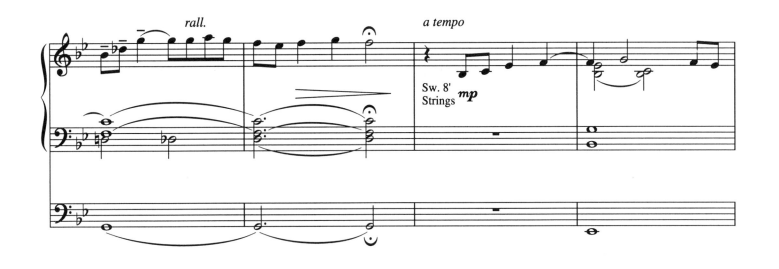

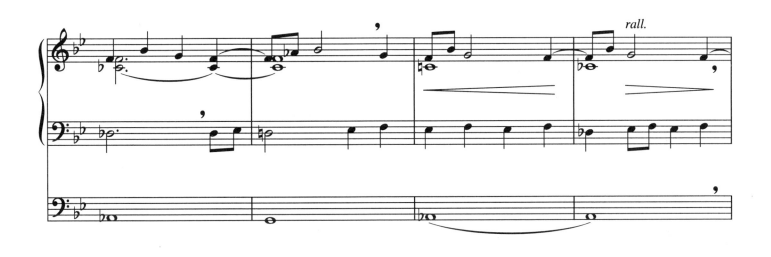

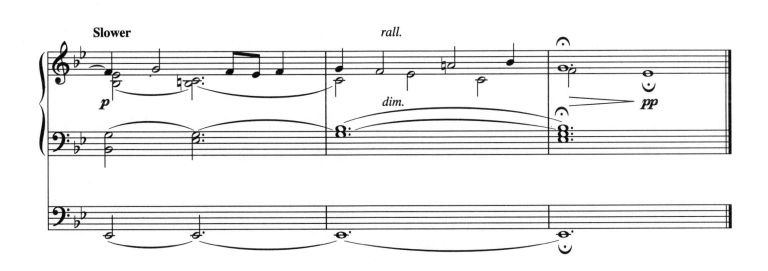

O COMFORTER, DRAW NEAR

Colin Hand

PEACE I LEAVE WITH YOU

Stanley Vann

25

SPIRITUS DOMINI

Richard Lloyd

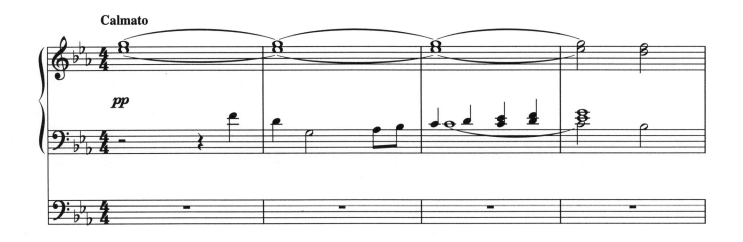

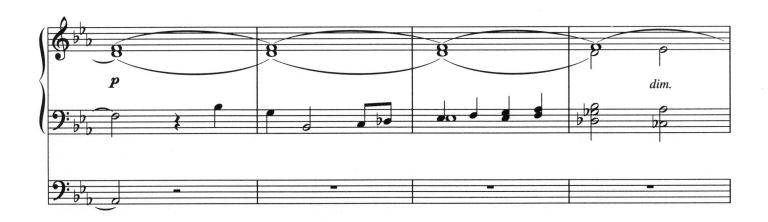

PRELUDE ON SALISBURY

Philip Moore

NON VOS RELINQUAM ORPHANOS

Andrew Gant

Andante poco mesto

POSTLUDE ON LLANFAIR

Dom Andrew Moore

Allegro moderato (♩ = c.84)

41

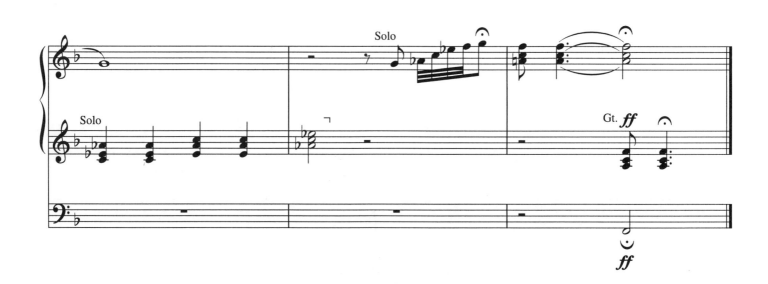

A RECESSIONAL FOR PENTECOST

Colin Mawby